MEL BAY PRESENTS

FAMOUS ROCK & BLUES
BASS PROGRESSIONS
BY CHRIS MATHEOS

2 3 4 5 6 7 8 9 0

QWIKGUIDE®

Visit us on the Web at www.melbay.com — E-mail us at email@melbay.com

Table of Contents

FAMOUS ROCK & BLUES PROGRESSIONS

There is no doubt that rock music's biggest infiuence is the blues. Most of rock music's most famous chord progressions are almost identical to famous blues progressions. The bass and drum parts may be a bit different in rock, but the progressions are almost identical.

Almost every chord progression in this book can be found in any era of rock and blues. The examples include chord changes, bass clef, and tab. This book covers many different styles of blues and rock. Having some understanding of the different style variations will make you a more complete bassist.

AUDIO RECORDING: The CD accompanying this book contains recordings of the examples. The first half of the CD includes the examples with bass, guitar, keys, and drums. The second half of the CD has all the examples with guitar, keys, and drums only. This way you can hear the bass grooves on the first half of the CD, and jam with the band on the second half. I encourage you to improvise your own variations to the written bass lines when jamming with the CD. The written bass lines are there to get you started with the basic groove. Get creative.

ABOUT THE BLUES

There is no single definition of the word "blues." It can be defined as a state of mind and the type of music that expresses that state of mind. It is about the most common style of music found at open mic nights. But it seems to be played very differently in every part of America.

It is believed that blues was first sung by slaves working in the fields of American plantations. After the American Civil War many slaves started moving north by way of the Mississippi River. The blues slowly moved up the river with them. Many of the relevant blues styles follow the river.

NEW ORLEANS BLUES: This style of blues has a strong percussive element to it. Many of the drum beats have a strong snare drum element to them. Many parade march beats were incorporated into the blues beats of New Orleans.

MEMPHIS BLUES: Some Memphis blues have a distinct funk feel. Other Memphis grooves mix a gospel feel into the blues.

DELTA BLUES: Delta blues styles are usually based around the Mississippi sound and are very traditional. Many of the chord progressions are very odd. Many songs use call and response. The progressions are often shaped to the vocalist. The band may stay on one chords for long periods of time, not changing to another chord until the vocalist cued it. Solo guitar/vocal is not uncommon in Delta blues.

CHICAGO BLUES: Chicago styles often incorporate shuffle grooves with harp and guitar. There are many small variations in Chicago blues. These variations often were geographical. The south side of town bands sounded different from the west side bands.

TEXAS BLUES: There seems to be a phenomenon called Texas blues. Most Texas blues sound similar to Chicago blues. In recent years some people have referred to Texas blues as a rock/blues mix. Some proper Texas blues styles use a root bounce feel with a shuffle. Other Texas blues mix swing and Zydeco feels into blues progressions.

CAJUN BLUES: New Orleans blues is not the only style fromLouisiana. Zydeco is a style from south western Louisiana. Zydeco mixes traditional Cajun and Creole music with contemporary instrumentation. There is also a French music element that came with the Cajun (Arcadian) settlers. Afro/Caribbean feels have also been incorporated into the style from the creole side. Many free/slaves and Hatian field workers were part of the culture. Zydeco often uses second line drum beats as well as 3/4 waltz grooves.

AUDIO CD: All the examples in this book are recorded with a full band on the accompanying CD. Each example is included with and without bass. This way you can hear what an example sounds like and then jam along with the band. Some examples play the progression once. Others play the progression two times. The bass sometimes plays basic pattern variations on the second time through the progression. This is called imporvisation. (variations not written out). Pattern variations are common in blues music. When you play along with the CD try to create your own pattern variations.

EXAMPLE 1: Basic Chicago shuffle over a standard twelve bar blues progression.

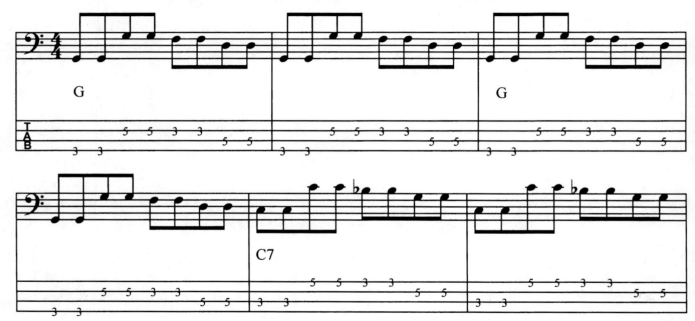

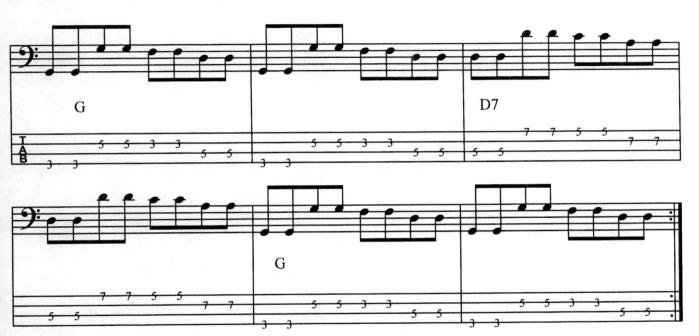

8

EXAMPLE 2: Twelve bar progression with rock n' roll feel.

Ex. 2 cont.

EXAMPLE 3: Twelve bar blues progression with a quarter note walking bass line.

Ex. 3 cont.

EXAMPLE 4: Walking shuffle bass line over twelve bar blues with quick four chord change.

Ex. 4 cont.

EXAMPLE 5: Twelve bar blues with a quick four change. The bass line is a typical Memphis funk groove. Bass lines like this had a large influence on 1970's pop music.

Ex. 5 cont.

EXAMPLE 6: 1970's rock n' roll feel.

Ex. 6 cont.

Ex. 6 cont.

EXAMPLE 7: Eight bar blues/rock progression.

EXAMPLE 8:

Ex. 8 cont.

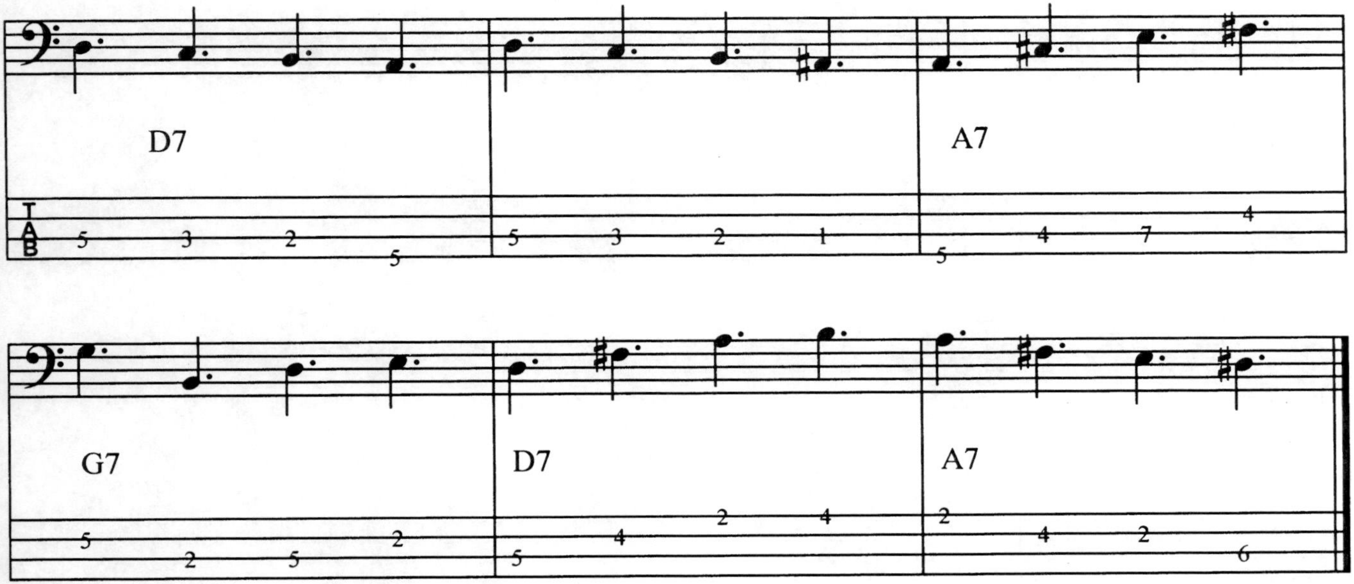

EXAMPLE 9: Gospel influenced blues progression.

Ex. 9 cont.

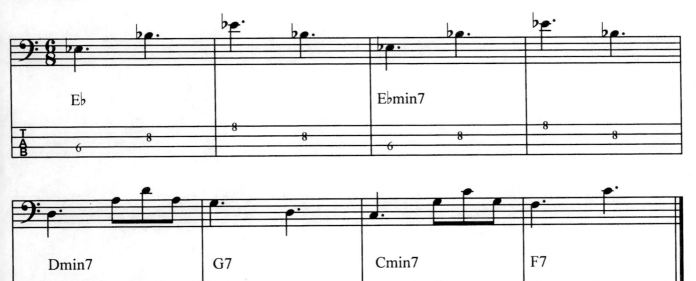

Ex.10: Swing style blues

Ex. 10 cont.

EXAMPLE 11: This example is a swing style blues. The progression is a twelve bar blues with jazz style substitutions.

Ex. 11 cont.

EXAMPLE 12: Twelve bar progression with a Texas blues/rock feel.

Ex. 12 cont.

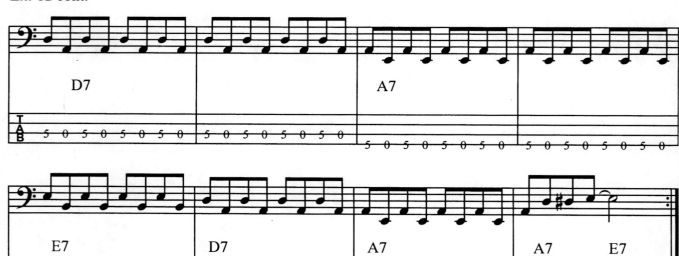

EXAMPLE 13: This example demonstrates a country blues feel over a twelve bar progression.

Ex. 13 cont.

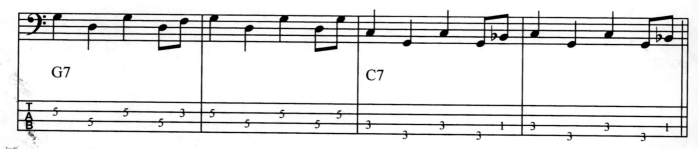

EXAMPLE 14: Slow 12/8 shuffle over twelve bar minor progression.

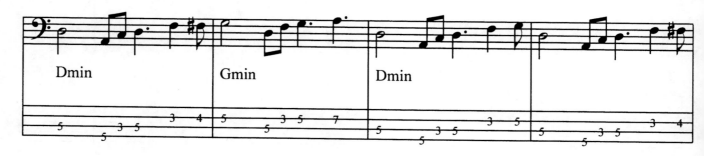

Ex. 14 cont.

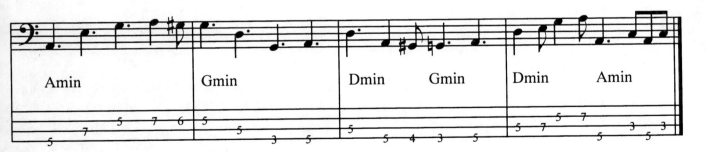

WHAT IS A PROGRESSION?

A chord progression is defined as a succession of two or more chords that have a harmonic relationship. A progression is what makes up a song: certain chords in a certain order. Many songs in blues and rock music use very simple progressions. There are endless songs with the identical progressions. The only difference between such songs is the lyrics and feel.

Many rock and blues musicians talk in numbers. They may say a song is in C. Then they will refer to the four chord or five chord. What does this mean? To understand number talk you must know the major scale.

C Major: C D E F G A B C

The Major scale uses eight notes. The first note is called the one or root. The second note is the two. The third note is the three, etc.

Say you are playing a blues in C. The band leader tells the band to start on the five chord. He is talking about the fifth note of the C major scale. This note is G. If the band leader told you to play a sharp five chord you would play G♯.

*This page has been
left blank to avoid
awkward page turns*

EXAMPLE 15:

Ex. 15 cont.

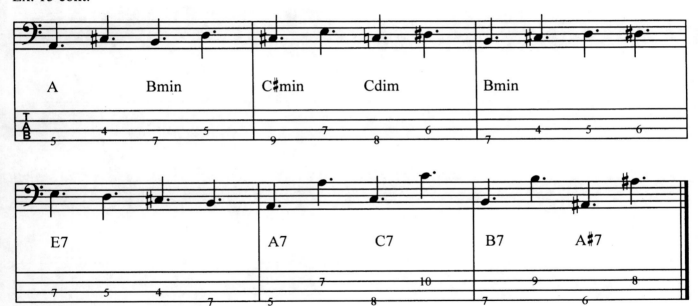

EXAMPLE 16:

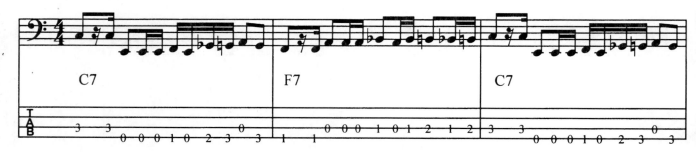

Ex. 16 cont.

EXAMPLE 17: Twelve bar progression with a Rock 'a' Billy feel.

Ex. 17 cont.

EXAMPLE 18:

Ex. 18 cont.

EXAMPLE 19:

Ex. 19 cont.

44

EXAMPLE 20: Twelve bar progression with a Chicago style feel.

Ex. 20 cont.

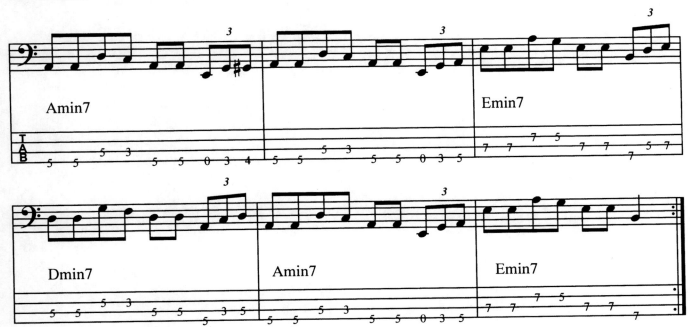

EXAMPLE 21: Louisiana feel often found in Zydeco music.

Ex. 21 cont.

C 7

D 7

EXAMPLE 22: Rock n' roll bass groove over a New Orleans/Zydeco second line drum beat.

Ex. 22 cont.

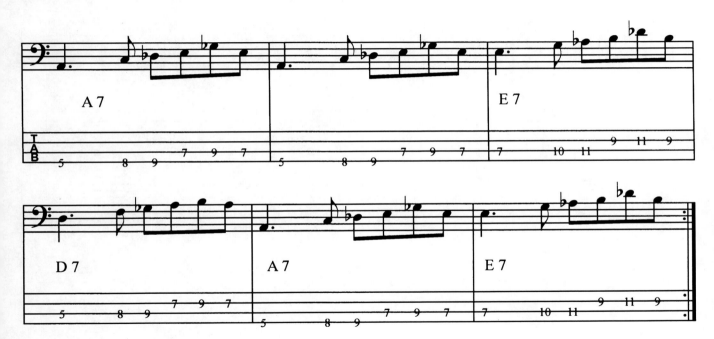

EXAMPLE 23: Twelve bar progression with a 1960's funk feel.

Ex. 23 cont.

EXAMPLE 24: Sixteen bar progression with a deep southern Gospel/blues feel.

Ex. 24 cont.

EXAMPLE 25: Twelve bar progression with Rock n' Roll eighth note feel.

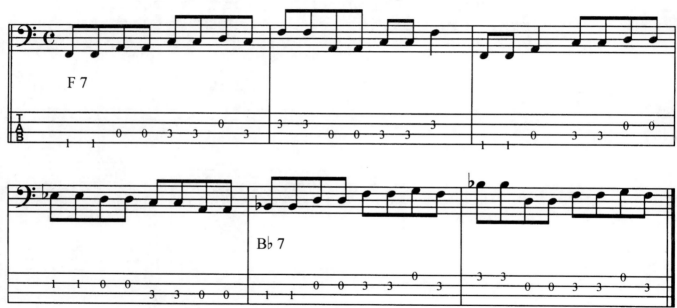

Ex. 25 cont.

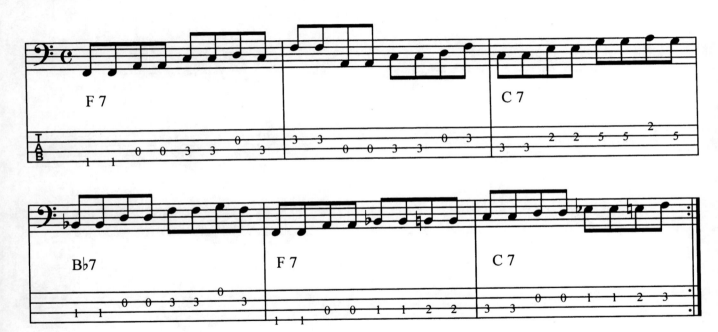

EXAMPLE 26: Sixteen bar progression with 6/8 Memphis gospel feel.

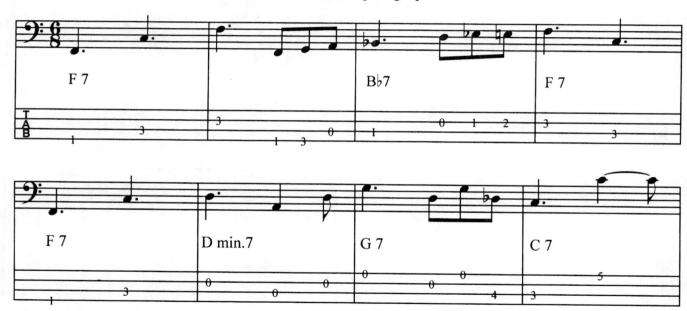

Ex. 26 cont.

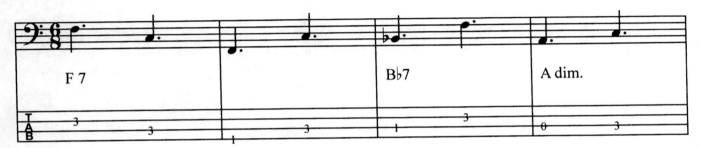

WHAT IS A VAMP?

Some blues/rock songs stay on one chord for a very long period of time. Some songs stay on one chord for the entire song. This is common when the singer uses improvised lyrics to tell a story. Story telling is not uncommon in Delta blues and Chicago blues. The rhythm section has to have strong endurance when backing up a story teller. Some story tellers really like to take their time. If you are vamping on a groove and get bored easily try getting creative with dynamics. Experimenting with volume levels in a vamp setting can really be fun for the band and the audience.

EXAMPLE 27: Vamp groove in 4/4 time.

A min. 7

EXAMPLE 28: Vamp groove in a Texas blues/rock feel.

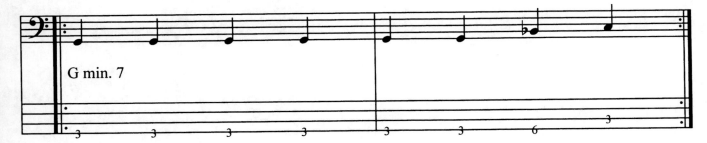

G min. 7

EXAMPLE 29: Vamp groove in 4/4.

EXAMPLE 30: Vamp groove in 4/4.

AUDIO CD: Recorded at: The Little Shack Studio in Rocky Point, NY (ex. 16-30)
Recorded at: The Mac Hayden Theater in Albany, NY (ex. 1-15)

KANE DAILY	guitar	tracks 20,22,
PETE EDSTROM	guitar	track 19
MIKE ERNST	guitar	track 21
KIP PACKARD	guitar	tracks 1-6, 7-16
RICK WAHLERS	guitars	tracks 17, 23-25, 27-30
KYLE WELCH	guitars	track 7
CARLTON STEWART	harp	tracks 18, 26
FRED PISCOP	keys	track 25
JOHN SCANLON	keys	track 23, 30
STEVE SEYDLER	keys	tracks 1-16
GREG GASCON	drums	tracks 1-17,20,23,25,
KEITH HURRELL	drums	tracks 18-19, 21-22, 24, 26-30

Tracks: 1-16 recorded by Steve Seydler, tracks 17-30 recorded by Chris Matheos.

BASSISTS: The following are a list of 10 Rock & Blues bassists that I have enjoyed studying the most over the years. Some I studied for their skilled riffs and some for their solid pocket playing.

BLUES BASSISTS:
Willie Dixon with Muddy Waters Band
Ernest Gatewood with Magic Sam
Jack Meyers with Buddy Guy
Joseph Brouchet with Clifton Chenier
Ernest Gatewood with Jimmy Dawkins

ROCK BASSISTS:
Billy Cox with Jimi Hendrix
Roger Glover with Deep Purple
Ule Ritgen with Electric Sun
John Entwistle with The Who
James Dewar with Robin Trower

ABOUT THE AUTHOR

Chris Matheos is a native of Rochester, NY. He studied music at The Berklee College of Music in Boston. He has published many instructional bass books with Mel Bay Publications. He has toured with national acts in about every style of music. He also performs and composes his own music and tours as a bass clinician. He endorses Washburn fretted basses, Keith Roscoe fretless basses, Conklin electric upright basses, Washburn acoustic/electric basses, David Eden amps, David Eden strings, and Pigtronix pedals.

OTHER BOOKS BY CHRIS MATHEOS:

PERCUSSIVE SLAP BASS...(MB95703BCD)

REGGAE GROOVES FOR ELECTRIC BASS........................(MB96722BCD)

100 FRETLESS BASS WORKOUTS ....(MB20702BCD)

100 ROCK & ROLL WORKOUTS FOR BASS ....(MB20703BCD)

FAMOUS JAZZ BASS CHORD PROGRESSIONS ....(MB98582BCD)

BASS WARM-UPS...(MB98433BCD)

50 TWO-HAND TAPPING WORKOUTS FOR BASS............(MB99365BCD)

50 MODAL SLAP BASS WORKOUTS ....(MB99364BCD)

BUILDING AMAZING BASS TECHNIQUE.........................(MB98434BCD)